## Dr Eric C

# History Through Objects
# The Condom

### Three thousand years of safer sex

**Translated by Patrick White**
**Illustrated by Pef**

When you're older and cold in bed, you can wear a willy warmer!

VIKING

VIKING

Published by the Penguin Group
Penguin Books Ltd, 27 Wrights Lane, London W8 5TZ, England
Penguin Books USA Inc., 375 Hudson Street, New York, New York 10014, USA
Penguin Books Australia Ltd, Ringwood, Victoria, Australia
Penguin Books Canada Ltd, 10 Alcorn Avenue, Toronto, Ontario, Canada M4V 3B2
Penguin Books (NZ) Ltd, 182–190 Wairau Road, Auckland 10, New Zealand

Penguin Books Ltd, Registered Offices: Harmondsworth, Middlesex, England

First published by Casterman 1993
Published simultaneously in Viking and Puffin 1995
1 3 5 7 9 10 8 6 4 2

Copyright © Casterman, 1993
Translation copyright © Patrick White, 1995
All rights reserved

Filmset in Linotron Bembo by
Rowland Phototypesetting Limited, Bury St Edmunds, Suffolk

Made and printed in Singapore

A CIP catalogue record for this book is available from the British Library

ISBN 0-670-85529-4

Photograph Credits

O. Chalumeau: cover, pages 8h, 9, 32, 38, 39, 41.
CRIPS: pages 8b, 25, 29, 34b, 37hg, 40, 41, 43, 47.
Giraudon: pages 12, 14d.
Réunion des musées nationaux: pages 13, 15, 31.
Roger-Viollet: pages 14h and b, 16, 21b.
Jean-Loup Charmet: pages 17, 18, 19.
Magnum: pages 21h (S. Salgado), 30 (E. Hartmann).
LRC Nederland: page 23.
Sipa Press: pages 27h, 37hd.
Condomerie, Amsterdam: page 26.
REA: page 27b.
Bulloz: page 28 (Rodin's *The Kiss*).
Museum of the History of Contraception, Toronto (Canada): page 33.
Keystone: page 32h.
Institut Pasteur (photographic science archives): pages 34h, 35.
Gilles Millet: page 37b.
Christophe L.: page 44.

# Contents

Condoms are as much part of our lives as the chewing-gum that sticks to our shoe. We carry them in our wallets, along with our student card. We keep them in our medicine cabinets with the aspirins. That's how much the condom has become accepted as a feature of our everyday life. They are handed out in the school yard, something which outrages some people but reassures others. So, come on, don't be embarrassed – be well read and not well dead! Because as my grandmother always used to say: 'Better safe than sorry . . .'

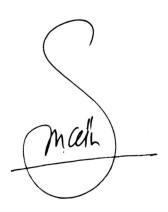

## Contraceptive and protective

The male condom is a narrow tube made from very thin natural latex rubber which is soft and stretchy. It is closed at one end, and fits over a man's erect penis during sexual intercourse in order to stop sperm entering the vagina and to prevent sexually transmitted diseases. The condom therefore has two main purposes: first, it is a means of contraception, and second, it is an effective means of protecting yourself (and other people) from sexually transmitted diseases (STDs). This is a rather po-faced way to describe a little object with a very long history.

*Originally made from all sorts of materials, sheep gut in particular, the majority of condoms are now made from latex, a natural product of the rubber tree. They are cylindrical in shape and have a diameter of 3.5 cm. When unrolled, they measure between 18 and 20 cm long. The latex is between 0.3 and 0.09 mm thick.*

*Even the dinosaurs became extinct.*

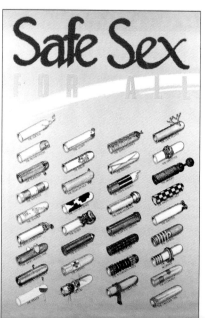

*Poster published in Holland, 1988.*

### A condom by any other name

*The world's imagination seems to be limitless when it comes to giving a name to this little object. A whole string of names have come and gone over the years and around the world: sheath, condom, rubber, and French letter, of course, but also 'capote anglaise' (English coat) in France, 'sock', 'hood' and 'bush hat' in Africa, 'Pariser' (Parisian) or 'Gummi' (rubber) in Vienna or Berlin, 'cocolock socks' in the West Indies, 'koteka' (penis gourd) in an Indonesian tribe, 'Port Said garter' elsewhere. An old name for it in France was 'redingote', an adaptation of the English 'riding coat'. So take your pick and use whichever name takes your fancy. Or, better still, why not make up your own?*

*rhaps they
d too many
condoms.*

*Rolled up and packaged
in small individual
sachets, male condoms
can be found in all
shapes and colours.
They may be straight,
contoured, flared,
ribbed, dotted or plain-
ended with no teat.
The packaging, the
brand, the flavour,
where they are sold
. . . there's an infinite
variety.*

*Women possibly have more erogenous zones than men. Erogenous zones are those which arouse desire when stimulated. The female orgasm, however, is experienced essentially in the clitoris and vagina. The clitoris is situated in the vulva. Like the penis in men, it is composed of erectile tissue. The vagina is a warm and moist passage which is very sensitive.*

**View of the uterus in cross-section.**

*Ovary*

## The mysteries of love

Sex is a matter of a few bodily organs, some physiological mechanisms and much mystery. Just let these different ingredients do their work and concentrate on the tenderness and magic of making love. But at the same time try to understand the most intimate workings of the human body. Ejaculation is the emission of semen through the opening at the end of the penis and can cause an intense sensation of pleasure. Semen consists of spermatic fluid in which spermatozoa swim. These are masculine reproductive cells which are produced in millions by the testicles. In women, ovulation – the production of an ovum by the ovaries – takes place each month between puberty and the menopause. This ovum travels down the Fallopian tube towards the uterus. About two-thirds of the way down the tube, if the ovum meets a sperm which (along with millions of others) has travelled from the vagina following a recent ejaculation, fertilization takes place. In other words, the first cell of a new human being is created.

**The path taken by the ovum.**

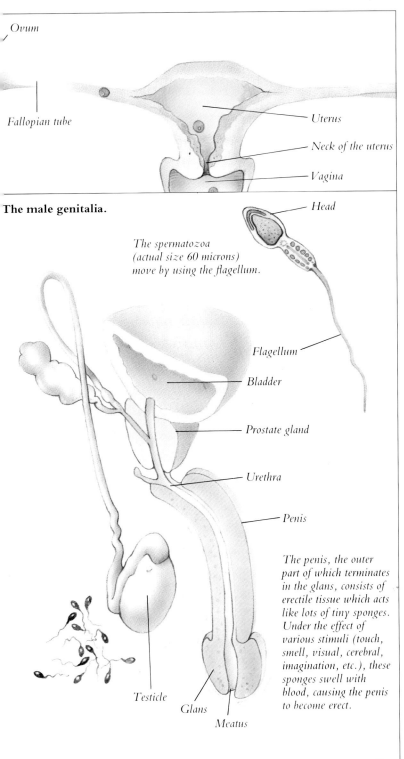

Ovum

Fallopian tube

Uterus

Neck of the uterus

Vagina

**The male genitalia.**

Head

The spermatozoa
(actual size 60 microns)
move by using the flagellum.

Flagellum

Bladder

Prostate gland

Urethra

Penis

The penis, the outer
part of which terminates
in the glans, consists of
erectile tissue which acts
like lots of tiny sponges.
Under the effect of
various stimuli (touch,
smell, visual, cerebral,
imagination, etc.), these
sponges swell with
blood, causing the penis
to become erect.

Testicle

Glans

Meatus

## A thousand-year-old invention

The condom goes back so far in time that it is impossible to say for certain when it was invented. Its story is bound up with historical anecdotes, fables and legends. The condom runs through history from the Cretan king Minos to the decisive invention of the vulcanization of rubber by the American Charles Goodyear in the middle of the nineteenth century. Its history is the history of sexuality, of birth control, and of the fight against sexual diseases.

*(Left: Bas-relief in Kadjuraho, India)*

# From antiquity to the 'French disease'

A prehistoric wall-painting depicts a type of condom, the ancient Egyptians wore them, though for different reasons, the Chinese were using oiled tissue paper some 4,000 years ago. It seems that the Greeks and the Romans were the first to use animal membranes as a contraceptive. The idea passed down through the centuries and was taken up again by Gabriele Fallopio, an Italian doctor, in the sixteenth century. He showed that its use was vitally important in the fight against the spread of syphilis (known as the 'English disease' in France and the 'French disease' in Britain), which was then raging through the population.

*Pillar representing the god Hermes (National Museum of Athens).*

*Erotic scene from a fresco in the Centurion's House in Pompeii.*

Was there really a Dr Condom? Absolutely! Some people attribute to him the discovery that sheep gut can be used as a contraceptive. This Dr Condom, or Conton, or even Colkborn, may have been a physician at the court of King Charles II in the seventeenth century. The main purpose of his invention may have been to protect the king from the many claims of his 'illegitimate children'!

Others say that the word condom comes from the Latin 'condere', meaning 'to hide'.

## Snakes and scorpions

King Minos of Crete is most famous for the labyrinth he built, on the advice of Daedalus, to contain the fearsome Minotaur. Legend also has it that the king's seed contained snakes and scorpions which killed his mistresses. It was suggested to him that he insert a goat's bladder into their vaginas, but he is said to have preferred to use bandages soaked in alum.

## The condom in literature

The very first mention of the condom goes back to prehistoric times: a fresco from the Combarelles grotto in the Dordogne region of France, dating from approximately 15,000–10,000 years BC, shows a man who appears to be 'sheathed' performing the sexual act. Thousands of years later, a play by Millet called *L'Ecole des filles (School for Girls)* refers to the use of 'un petit linge' (a small cloth) with contraceptive properties. And on this side of the Channel, a book published in 1741 entitled *A Panegyric upon Cundum* celebrated a certain Colonel Cundum. Madame de Sevigné, Casanova, the Marquis de Sade, Guy de Maupassant, Flaubert, Proust and many others have all written about it, often praising it but sometimes in less flattering terms.

Madame de Sévigné (1626–96) is supposed to have said some very uncomplimentary things about the condom, calling it 'armour against pleasure and a spider's web against danger'. Fortunately the sensitivity and quality of condoms have improved a lot since those days. The well-established reputation of Victor Hugo (1802–85) as a vigorous lover seems to be confirmed by this anecdote told by the Goncourt brothers in their diary: when he left Guernsey the author of Les Misérables is said to have left a stock of 'gigantic French letters' in a cupboard.

*William Shakespeare (1564–1616) refers to it amusingly as 'the Venus glove'.*

Casanova (1725–98) is reported to have said: 'I will never do myself up in a dead animal skin to prove that I'm alive.' By 1758, however, he had changed his mind: 'Ten years ago I would have called this an invention of the devil but I now believe that its inventor must have been a good man.'

### Thank you, Mr Goodyear!

In the middle of the nineteenth century the American Charles Goodyear invented a revolutionary process called vulcanization, which consisted in treating the natural sap of the rubber tree. Thereafter it was possible to produce good-quality rubber in large quantities. It didn't take people long to think up a use for the new invention in our private lives, and thus the modern condom was invented. However, latex condoms as we know them today were not developed until just before the Second World War.

## A natural product

A condom begins its life in the rubber tree. A long cut is made in the bark to let the sap flow out. The sap is collected at the base of the tree, purified and then centrifuged. After vulcanization (heating with sulphur), small glass moulds are immersed in the large tanks containing the latex. The condoms are then powdered (usually with talc) in order to extract them from the moulds.

'If everyone in the world were to use condoms, would rubber trees become extinct?' I hear you environmentally aware people ask. Well, the answer is no, as the manufacture of condoms represents only a tiny proportion of the world's consumption of rubber.

*A large tree of the Euphorbia family, the rubber tree used to grow wild in South America. Today it is cultivated mainly in south-east Asia (Malaysia and Indonesia) and, to a lesser degree, in Amazonia and Central Africa.*

The making of the cut in the tree is a skill that has been passed on from generation to generation. The sap (or latex, from the Latin word meaning 'liquid') flows into a special container.

21

## Condoms under the microscope

The first manufacturer of condoms on an industrial scale was a certain Mr Macintosh, the famous maker of raincoats. Today condoms must pass the strict tests of the British Standards Institution in order to gain a Kitemark on their packs. Every condom is electrically screened on the production line to check for holes and thin spots. Other more stringent tests such as the airburst test are part of the European Standard for condoms, which is due to replace the British Standard BS3704. A *Which?* report published in August 1993 suggests that poor-quality condoms are few and far between. But they point out that no one has yet developed a reliable means of testing that simulates the stresses and strains that a condom undergoes during sexual intercourse. Those passing the airburst test are less likely to break in use.

**Highly concentrated production**

*Condoms can only be produced in factories with a large capacity, as the tanks containing the latex must operate round the clock. Even the smallest factories produce several tens of millions of condoms a year. Although most of the raw material comes from Asia, the three biggest producers in the world are Japan, Britain and the USA.*

*After the vulcanization process, glass moulds give the condoms their final shape.*

Before the Kitemark is issued, a series of tests are made to check the quality, strength and purity of the condom and the lubricant, if there is one. The testers measure the dimensions and volume and check that the condom has no leaks. The airburst test inflates the condom to a pressure of 15 litres of compressed air (considerably more than in normal conditions!). If it doesn't burst, it passes the test.

## How to use a male condom

Condoms are very simple to use and, as long as you do so properly, are very effective.

- A condom must never be used more than once, so don't go giving it a wash after you have used it and hanging it out

on the clothes line for the next time you strike lucky!

- Be careful not to tear it with your fingernails when you take it out of the wrapper.
- Make sure the rolled-up rim is on the outside of the condom as you put it on.
- The condom must be rolled down over the whole erect penis before penetration takes place.
- The man must withdraw immediately after ejaculating, holding the condom at its base. Make a knot in it before disposing of it.

Show off!

### A lonely discovery

*Even though it's the simplest thing in the world to do, putting on a condom, especially for the first time, can be an embarrassing experience. Try getting to know this strange little object alone in the privacy of your own bedroom before you contemplate using one when making love*

T'S MAGIC!

Verführen mit Kondom.
Lust beginnt,
wo die Angst aufhört.

## Keep away from heat

*Latex does not like heat. Condoms should be kept in a cool place, away from direct light if possible. They can, however, be carried around perfectly safely, perhaps in a little box.*

## Danger Vaseline!

*People are sometimes tempted to use Vaseline, cream or even cooking oil to lubricate the condom but this must be avoided at all costs, as all these fatty substances can damage the latex. Instead use a water-based lubricating gel, which can be bought from most chemists, or buy condoms that are already lubricated.*

## Where and how much?

 Only a few years ago, going out to buy condoms was like going on a dangerous mission. You had to endure the chemist's suspicious look as you whispered to him what you wanted, desperately hoping that he wouldn't shout to his assistant to ask him where the condoms were hidden away.

Times have changed, and buying a condom is now as easy as buying a box of matches. You can still get them from chemists but now they are displayed openly on stands. You can also get them from garages, record shops, supermarkets, by mail order, from vending machines, in colleges, leisure centres and, of course, from family planning clinics.

### How much does it cost?

*It costs about 6p to produce a condom but how much you pay for it depends on where you buy it, the brand and how many there are in a pack. From a mail order catalogue you may pay around £3 for a pack of twelve, while in a chemist's this could cost between £4 and £5, or about £1.25 for three. Condoms are currently free at Family Planning clinics.*

Don't worry, young man. I understand perfectly.

*In New York, Amsterdam and London there are shops which sell nothing but condoms of every possible variety. They mostly stock novelty condoms, which haven't always proved to be safe.*

### Female Condoms

*There is a female condom called Femidom currently on sale in the United Kingdom. Its purpose is the same as the male condom but it is made of polyurethane rather than latex rubber. Closed at one end, it is designed to form a loose lining to a woman's vagina and has two flexible rings, one at each end, to keep it in place. Other types of female condom are expected on the market in the future.*

*Femidom cost about £1 each.*

## Love and protection

The condom used to be associated with loose morals, with soldiers setting off to war, or with prostitutes, but now it has become part of everyone's life, regardless of their age or sex, performing its dual role as a contraceptive and a means of protection against sexually transmitted diseases, including AIDS.

### 'When a man loves a woman . . .'

The male condom is not, despite its name, something that just concerns men – far from it. Today it's a matter for all of us, male and female. Studies show that a growing number of teenage girls and young women are becoming concerned about AIDS and venereal diseases (the word venereal comes from Venus, the goddess of love). They want to use a condom to protect themselves and their partner. Many of them refuse to have sex without one. It would be incorrect to say that the sensation is the same whether you use a condom or not, but there is a lot more to making love, the pleasure that men and women feel, than just friction. Using a contraceptive has never stopped anyone from experiencing pleasure. Some people even say that, on the contrary, it means that you can make love feeling completely relaxed. You don't need to think about anything except how good it feels to be with your partner.

**Fully comprehensive insurance**
*The condom also protects against other STDs such as forms of nonspecific urethritis and chlamydia. If you do have an infection you must tell your partner, since some diseases have no visible symptoms.*

**A word to the wise**
*Instead of waiting for him or her to 'get one', why not keep a condom in your pocket, bag or wallet?*

*'Homme et la Femme, a painting by Pierre Bonnard (1867–1947) in the Musée d'Orsay in Paris.*

## Break the ice

*tudies have shown that most young people (both boys and girls) are prepared to se a condom . . . if the other person suggests it! But either for fear of being laughed or because of shyness, they still don't dare say anything, even though that is just hat their partner is waiting for. So why not speak up and break the ice?*

## My body, my choice

The reason why condoms have been used as a contraceptive for so long is that the principle behind them is so simple. However, with the introduction of the Pill in the sixties, the condom became used less and less for birth control as the Pill was more convenient and more effective. In fact, people were always pointing out the wonderful babies born as a result of the condom's failure. It is, however, perfectly reliable as long as it is used properly and regularly – in other words every time you have sex. There are other effective methods of contraception apart from the condom: the Pill, which is reliable and safe except for women who smoke; the coil, a small object placed in the uterus by the doctor to prevent the egg from being fertilized (however, some women's bodies reject these); and male or female sterilization, which has the disadvantage of being permanent. But be careful, don't confuse contraception with the prevention of venereal disease.

*The contraceptive pill was invented in 1956 in the United States but it took years of persuasion, determination and scientific progress to make it a reality. Its development was made possible by a tenacious woman, Margaret Sanger (1879–1966), and a skilled team of scientists led by Dr Pincus. Now that it has been refined, the Pill is used by a majority of young women.*

### Ogino babies
*There are two other methods which in practice have been shown to have a high failure rate: coitus interruptus before ejaculation, and the Ogino method, named after the Japanese doctor who advocated abstinence from sex for certain times during the menstrual cycle, around the fourteenth day when ovulation takes place.*

This poster, produced by the Museum of the History of Contraception in Toronto, Canada, shows the many means of contraception used by men and women since antiquity. The Catholic Church categorically condemns 'artificial' contraception, believing that the sole purpose of sex is to conceive children.

## Love hurts

In June 1981 an American scientific journal reported some cases of a disease which aroused the curiosity of the medical community. It was the first mention of what was to become the great epidemic of the end of the twentieth century: AIDS. AIDS has placed the condom spectacularly back in the limelight, as it is today the **only way** of preventing the virus from being transmitted sexually – apart, of course, from abstaining from sex altogether and fidelity between two partners who have had AIDS tests to prove that they are not carrying the virus.

*It is essential to prevent HIV, the virus that causes AIDS, from being transmitted, because as yet there is no vaccine to inoculate people against it and no treatment to counteract it and the various diseases it causes. There are some drugs available today which improve the lives of sufferers, but they must be taken under close medical supervision and their effect lasts only for a few years. Finding a vaccine to fight the virus is a considerable challenge, as the nature of the HIV virus is constantly changing.*

*'Please kiss me even if I have got AIDS. I can't make you ill.'* (Mexican poster)

### Tolerance and solidarity

*The fight against AIDS is both a fight against its spread and a fight against the marginalization of sufferers. It is unacceptable that victims should have to feel rejection and that, for example, a five-year-old child should be sent home from a holiday camp because he is HIV-positive. We must each show tolerance and solidarity in the face of this prejudice*

The HIV virus, which
is very short-lived
when exposed to air,
can be transmitted in
just three ways: first,
sexually from a man to
a woman or another
man, or from a woman
to a man or another
woman; second, in the
blood (from sharing
unsterilized syringes);
and third, from a
pregnant woman to her
unborn child, which
accounts for about one
in every four or five
cases. It cannot be
transmitted through
normal day-to-day
behaviour: at school, in
the swimming-pool, on
the bus or the tube . . .
or from a mosquito bite!

Being HIV-positive
means that you are
carrying the virus and
can transmit it. It does
not mean that you have
got AIDS, but that it
might develop after
two, five, ten or more
years. The time will
vary from person to
person. Inside the body
the virus attacks certain
cells, mainly a
particular type of white
blood cell, T4
lymphocytes. These
frontline soldiers of the
immune system protect
us from infections.
Over the years the
virus multiplies and
gradually begins to
disrupt the immune
system. This is how
HIV infection develops
into full-blown
AIDS, AIDS being
an acronym for
Acquired Immune
Deficiency Syndrome.

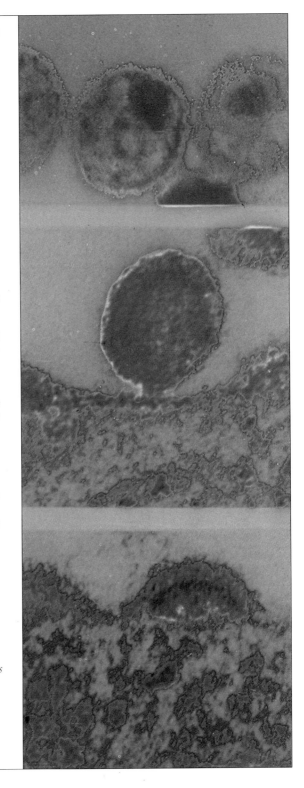

# A challenge for the Third World

Although the AIDS epidemic now affects the whole world, the situation is currently most drastic in sub-Saharan Africa. Even though it is extremely difficult to say for certain what will happen, certain figures speak for themselves. It is estimated that nearly 13 million men and women have been infected since the beginning of the epidemic, and that over a million have already developed AIDS. In some maternity hospitals in cities situated near Lake Victoria, a third of the women who come to give birth are carriers of the AIDS virus.

Another thing to bear in mind is that as vaccines and effective treatments begin to be found, the gap between the rich countries which will be able to afford the drugs and the poor countries which won't will grow. Only a genuine spirit of cooperation between the countries of the world can change this situation. There is a risk that the drama being played out at the moment in Africa will be repeated in Latin America and especially in Asia, where there has recently been a spectacular spread of the epidemic.

Over and above its human consequences, the considerable social and economic effects of AIDS on individuals and families seem set to hinder further the development of African countries already faced with serious difficulties. The countries are now taking action to inform their people, with the support of organizations promoting international cooperation. Efforts made so far, however, fall far short of what is needed.

**One day you too, white or black, will find yourself defenceless.**

*In Gisenyi (in Rwanda), Mummy Christine, who is sixty-nine years old, has set up a reception centre for about sixty children whose parents have died from AIDS.*

CONTRE LE SIDA : UTILISER LE PRESERVATIF

AGAINST AIDS : USE A CONDOM

*Illustration taken from a picture book on AIDS published in Cameroon in 1989.*

*Poster from Thailand, 1989.*

# It takes all sorts to make a world

More than 10,000 million condoms are sold each year throughout the world. Each country pays a lot of attention to the external appearance of the packaging, which ranges from the very sober to the very playful depending on whom they are aimed at. Some people have even began to collect them. The Japanese are the biggest consumers, with about 70 per cent of couples claiming that they use them, as against 35 to 40 per cent in Britain, more than 10 per cent in the USA and 7 per cent in France, the lowest figure among industrialized countries.

*Condoms made from sheep gut are extremely sensitive. Despite being more pleasurable, they also break more easily and are five to six times more expensive.*

*Humour is used a lot in Japan to market condoms. Each of these packets is supposed to correspond to the blood group of its user.*

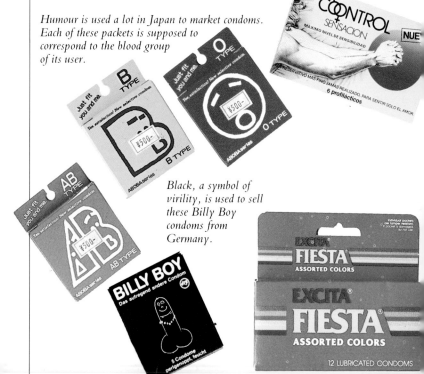

*Black, a symbol of virility, is used to sell these Billy Boy condoms from Germany.*

### Let's talk about AIDS

Unsafe sex and shared drugs needles are how people catch AIDS. A condom will prevent the virus passing between sexual partners, as it causes a barrier between them. A disposable needle, used once, is the only way for drug users to avoid injecting infected blood. Moralizers say that AIDS is the result of sexual freedom and the so-called drug culture, but you only need to have sexual contact *once* with a carrier or use a dirty needle *once* – so GET WISE and STAY SAFE. If you're going to have sex, USE A CONDOM.

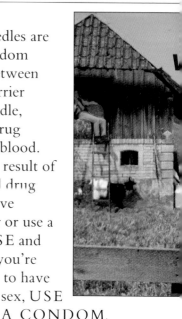

**rendez-vous**

STOP SIDA

**tonight**

STOP SIDA

**ok**

STOP SIDA

STOP SIDA

*In 1989 the Swiss Federal Office of Public Health took action and launched this visually striking campaign. (SIDA is the AIDS acronym in French.)*

40

STOP AIDS

## Questions and Answers about AIDS (Compiled by the Terrence Higgins Trust)

Q. Can heterosexuals become infected with HIV?

A. *Yes. HIV is an equal-opportunities virus which does not discriminate by sex, colour, age or religious belief. It can be transmitted from an infected male to a female, and from an infected female to a male.*

Q. I have read that the AIDS virus is present in tears and saliva. If that is true, can you become infected from kissing?

A. *The AIDS virus can be found in the saliva and tears of some infected people, but not all. It can be isolated in laboratory conditions, but not in large enough quantities to be infectious, so crying and kissing are still fine.*

Q. My girlfriend and I are having this argument. She wants me to use a condom so she won't have to go on the Pill. I say no, because rubbers are not 100 per cent reliable. Who's right?

A. *Don't get mixed up about contraceptives used for birth control and condoms used for disease control. The Pill will not protect anyone from sexually transmitted diseases, so it is essential to use a condom during sex to protect both of you. You're right: condoms are not 100 per cent reliable. They can break, especially if they are not used properly or if they're used without lubrication. Use lots of water-based lubricant, like KY, and not an oil-based one.*

Q. I am not gay and I don't use drugs. Why should I worry about AIDS?

A. *Keep in mind that it is behaviour that places you at risk, not a label. Think in terms of risky behaviour, not risk groups, and you will see more clearly why anyone could be involved. When you start a relationship with someone, you don't necessarily know their sexual or drug-use history, and they may not know all about the people they have had relationships with in the past.*

41

# Young people speak their minds

The British Wellness Council was set up by the British Safety Council. They run a National Condom Week each year with the aim of encouraging more people, young and old, to use condoms. 'Slip into something safe and sexy' was the slogan of one of their campaigns. So what do young people think of the condom?

*'The first time I bought them from a chemist's . . . I freaked, it was awful . . . Now I'm so used to buying them that it's almost become a game for me. I deliberately ask women sales assistants, just to see how they react.' (Thomas)*

*'A condom is to stop AIDS, to stop STDs and to stop you getting pregnant. It annoys me a little that it's all been lumped together. You talk about love to adults and they just go on about condoms.' (Nathalie)*

*'When I met Camille she made me use a condom . . . I'd never used one with other girls. When we made love it was so good. I'd never known it like that before.' (Anthony)*

*'It was on holiday and we made love without using a condom. I wasn't worried at all, I was on the pill . . . But after I saw a programme about AIDS on the TV I started to get anxious . . .' (Carol)*

*'Even though we are very close, it hasn't stopped us using a condom since we started having sex.' (Djamila and Jacky)*

*'If I go out with a boy I like I'll definitely ask him to wear a condom, even if I know him well and trust him.' (Sarah)*

'It's my first fancy-dress party!

Thomas, the condom in every guise.

*Posters published by the French AIDS Prevention Agency in 1991.*

'I've always had an excellent relationship with sex.

Fulbert, the worldly condom.

# Further information

## To read

The Terrence Higgins Trust HIV/AIDS Book, *by Judy Tavanyer, Thorsons, 1992.*

The Impact of Aids, *by Ewan Armstrong, Franklin Watts, 1990.*

Love Talk: A Young Person's Guide to Sex, Love and Life, *by Eleanor Stephens, Virago, 1991.*

Making It: How to Handle Love, *by Tricia Kreitman, Pan, 1993.*

What's Happening to My Body? A Growing-up Guide for Parents and Sons, *and* What's Happening to My Body? A Growing-up Guide for Parents and Daughters, *by Lynda Madaras, Penguin, 1989 (revised).*

## The statistics of the epidemic

As of 28 February 1994 there were 8,842 reported cases of AIDS in the United Kingdom, with the number of people carrying the virus at 21,101. In September 1992 there were 23,924 cases of AIDS in France, 15,698 in Spain, 14,783 in Italy, 2,691 in Switzerland and 1,224 in Belgium.

### Beware of sero-conversion
*You must wait three months after possible contamination before having an HIV test. This period of time is needed for the antibodies which the test is meant to detect to appear in the blood.*

### For help and information

If you want to find out more about condoms or any other method of contraception, or want to know where your nearest family planning clinic is, just contact the FPA by phone or by letter. Please send a stamped addressed envelope if writing.

FPA National Office
27–45 Mortimer Street
London W1N 7RJ
Telephone: 071-636 7866

FPA Wales
4 Museum Place
Cardiff CF1 3BG
Telephone: 0222-342766

FPA Northern Ireland
113 University Street
Belfast BT7 1HP
Telephone: 0232-325488

FPA Scotland
Contact FPA London
for details.

The Brook Advisory Centre
Telephone: 071-708 1234
Sessions for young people
under 25.

National AIDS Helpline
For free 24-hour advice
Telephone: 0800-567 123

Terrence Higgins Trust
Helpline
Telephone: 071-620 7000

When I grow up, can you remind me to protect the whale, the forests, the elephants and the ozone layer?

Don't forget to protect love as well.